200 HYMN IMPROVIS

AFTER THE LAST VERSE

MALCOLM ARCHER

Kevin Mayhew

We hope you enjoy the music in this book.
Further copies are available from your local music shop or Christian bookshop.

In case of difficulty, please contact the publisher direct by writing to:

The Sales Department
KEVIN MAYHEW LTD
Buxhall, Stowmarket
Suffolk IP14 3BW

Phone 01449 737978
Fax 01449 737834
Email info@kevinmayhewltd.com

Please ask for our complete catalogue of outstanding Church Music.

Acknowledgements

The publishers wish to express their gratitude to the following
for permission to use copyright material.

Oxford University Press, 70 Baker Street, London W1M 1DJ for *Abbot's Leigh*, *Down Ampney*, *Forest Green*, *Gonfalon Royal*, *King's Lynn*, *Kingsfold*, *Monks Gate*, *Woodlands* and *Wolvercote*.

The John Ireland Trust, 35 St Mary's Mansions, St Mary's Terrace, London W2 1SQ
for *Love Unknown*.

The Executors of the late Dr Basil Harwood, Stewart House, 24 Kingsway, London WC2B 6JX
for *Luckington* and *Thornbury*.

J. Curwen & Sons Ltd, 8/9 Frith Street, London W1V 5TZ for *Little Cornard* and *Marching*.

The Canterbury Press, St Mary's Works, St Mary's Plain, Norwich NR3 3BH
for *Amen Court* and *Bow Brickhill*.

Novello & Co Ltd, 8/9 Frith Street, London W1V 5TZ for *Michael*.

First published in Great Britain in 1995 by Kevin Mayhew Ltd

© Copyright 1995 Kevin Mayhew Ltd

ISMN M 57004 851 9
ISBN 0 86209 502 6
Catalogue No: 1400048

Cover design by Jonathan Stroulger
Music editor: Joanne Clarke
Music setting by Kevin Whomes

Printed and bound in Great Britain

Contents

Foreword

The idea for this book came as the result of a cry for help from many organists whom I have encountered over the years who find improvising the hardest aspect of organ playing. Unfortunately, it is one thing which they are called upon to do time and time again. *After the Last Verse* is an attempt to provide useful and attractive service music based on the hymns; short extemporary pieces which may be used to fill in after the hymn has finished, at moments like the Offertory, or during a procession. Most of these pieces are about sixteen bars in length, but they can easily be shortened if necessary by playing perhaps the final four or eight bars, depending upon what is needed. They may also be lengthened by repeating the final section. Most of all, I hope that these short pieces will provide ideas and encouragement to the faint of heart to have a go at their own improvisations.

The pieces also have other uses: several will make short voluntaries or reflectional works which can be used before a service or during the Communion. Some may also be used in place of or preceding the play-over of the hymn, and others as an interlude before the final verse. For this reason, some arrangements have been included in two keys, for those occasions where the hymn books differ.

I have not suggested registrations, since this will vary according to the instrument available. However, several of the pieces indicate the use of a solo stop on one manual with an accompaniment on another, though many will adapt to single keyboard instruments or organs without pedals. Some of the pieces will work equally well when played loudly or softly, and where this is the case dynamics have been omitted. The tempo of each piece will normally be directly related to the tempo of the associated hymn, but tempo markings have been provided for when these pieces are used independently.

The player should, in the spirit of extemporisation, feel free to adapt the piece to suit each particular instrument or occasion. Though many of the pieces in this book are quite easy to read at sight, they are in no sense an attempt to write down to players of modest ability. The hope is that many organist in lofts of all altitudes will find this a useful resource book!

Malcolm Archer

1 ABBOT'S LEIGH

Based on the hymn tune by Cyril Taylor (1907-1991)

2 ABERYSTWYTH

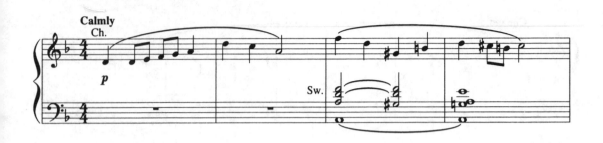

OR

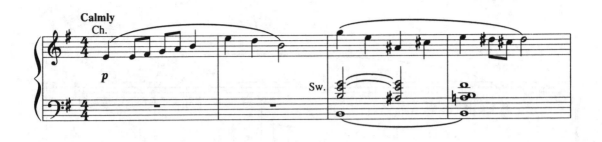

Based on the hymn tune by Joseph Parry (1841-1903)

3 ABRIDGE

Based on the hymn tune by Isaac Smith (1734-1805)

4 ADESTE FIDELES

See over for another key

OR

Based on the hymn tune by John Francis Wade (1711-1786)

5 ALL FOR JESUS

Based on the hymn tune by John Stainer (1840-1901)

6 ALL SAINTS

OR

Based on a melody from the Geistreiches Gesangbuch (1698) adapted by William Henry Monk (1823-1889)

7 ALL THINGS BRIGHT AND BEAUTIFUL

Based on the hymn tune by William Henry Monk (1823-1889)

8 AMEN COURT

See over for another key

OR

Based on the hymn tune by John Dykes Bower (1905-1981)

9 ANGEL VOICES

Based on the hymn tune by Edwin George Monk (1819-1900)

10 ANIMA CHRISTI

OR

Based on the hymn tune by William Maher (1823-1877)

11 AR HYD Y NOS

Based on a traditional Welsh melody

12 AURELIA

See over for another key

OR

Based on the hymn tune by Samuel Sebastian Wesley (1810-1876)

13 AUS DER TIEFE

Based on a melody from the Nürnbergisches Gesangbuch (1676)

14 AUSTRIA

Based on a Croation folk tune adapted by Franz Joseph Haydn (1732-1809)

15 AVE VIRGO VIRGINUM

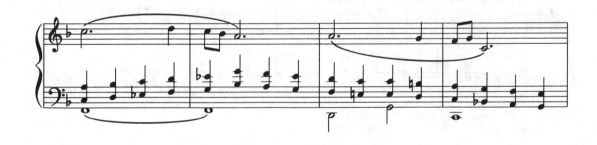

See over for another key

OR

Based on a traditional melody from Leisentritt's Catholicam Hymnologium Germanicum (1584)

16 BILLING

With flowing movement

See over for another key

OR

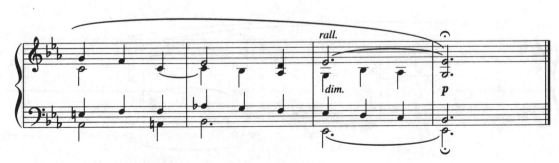

Based on the hymn tune by Richard Runciman Terry (1865-1938)

17 BINCHESTER

See over for another key

OR

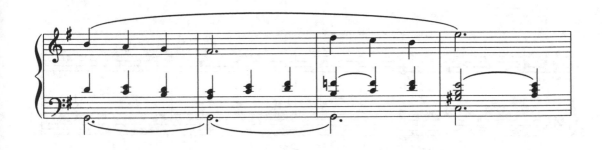

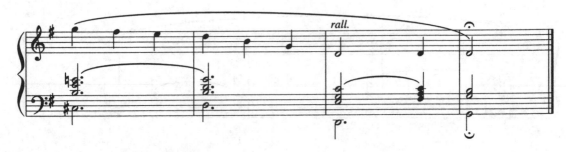

Based on the hymn tune by William Croft (1678-1727)

18 BISHOPTHORPE

Based on the hymn tune by Jeremiah Clarke (c.1673-1707)

19 BLAENWERN

OR

Based on the hymn tune by William Rowlands (1860-1937)

20 BOW BRICKHILL

Based on the hymn tune by Sydney Hugo Nicholson (1875-1947)

© Copyright The Canterbury Press Norwich

21 BRISTOL

Based on a melody from Thomas Ravencroft's Psalmes (1621)

22 BROTHER JAMES'S AIR

OR

Based on the hymn tune by Brother Leith MacBeth Bain (c.1860-1925)

23 BUCKLAND

Based on the hymn tune by Leighton George Hayne (1836-1883)

24 BUNESSAN

With lilting movement

If a shorter piece is required, start from 𝄋 or ⊕

Based on a traditional Gaelic melody

41

25 CAITHNESS

OR

Based on a melody from the Scottish Psalter (1635)

26 CAPETOWN

Based on the hymn tune by Friedrich Filitz (1804-1876)

27 CARLISLE

Based on the hymn tune by Charles Lockhart (1745-1815)

28 CASWALL

OR

Based on the hymn tune by Friedrich Filitz (1804-1876)

29 CHORUS ANGELORUM

Based on the hymn tune by Arthur Somervell (1863-1937)

30 CONTEMPLATION

See over for another key

OR

Based on the hymn tune by Frederick Arthur Gore Ouseley (1825-1889)

31 CRADLE SONG

This may be repeated with the RH one octave higher

Based on the hymn tune by William James Kirkpatrick (1838-1921)

32 CRANHAM

Based on the hymn tune by Gustav Holst (1874-1934)

33 CRIMOND

Based on the hymn tune by Jessie Seymour Irvine (1836-1887)

34 CROFT'S 136th

Based on the hymn tune by William Croft (1678-1727)

35 CROSS OF JESUS

See over for another key

OR

Based on the hymn tune by John Stainer (1840-1901)

36 CRÜGER

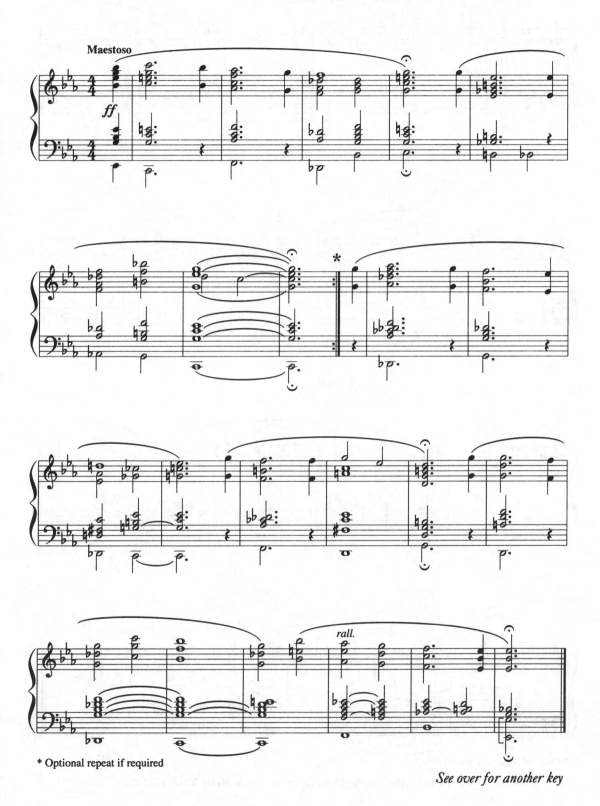

Maestoso

ff

* Optional repeat if required

See over for another key

OR

* Optional repeat if required

Based on the hymn tune by Johann Crüger (1598-1662) adapted by William Henry Monk (1823-1889)

37 CULBACH

See over for another key

OR

Based on the hymn tune adapted from Johann Scheffler's Heilige Seelenlust (1657)

38 CWM RHONDDA

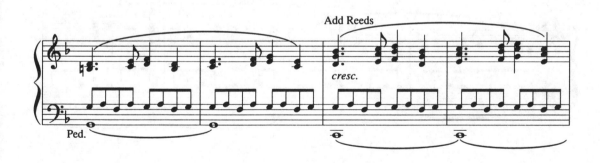

See over for another key

OR

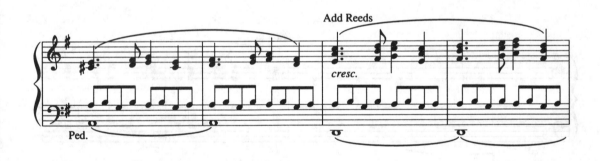

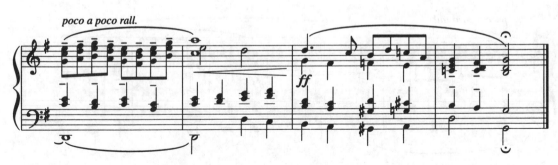

Based on the hymn tune by John Hughes (1873-1932)

39 DARWALL'S 148th

Based on the hymn tune by John Darwall (1731-1789)

40 DEUS TUORUM MILITUM

OR

Man. (or Ped.)

Based on a melody from the Grenoble Antiphener (1753)

41 DIADEMATA

Based on the hymn tune by George Job Elvey (1816-1893)

42 DIX

Based on the hymn tune by Conrad Kocher (1786-1872) adapted by William Henry Monk (1823-1889)

43 DOMINUS REGIT ME

Based on the hymn tune by John Bacchus Dykes (1823-1876)

44 DOWN AMPNEY

Based on the hymn tune by Ralph Vaughan Williams (1872-1958)

45 DUKE STREET

Based on the hymn tune by John Hatton (d. 1793)

46 DUNDEE

Based on a melody from the Scottish Psalter (1615)

47 EASTER HYMN

Based on a melody from the Lyra Davidica (1708)

48 EIN' FESTE BURG

74

rall.

See over for another key

75

OR

Based on the hymn tune by Martin Luther (1483-1546)

49 EISENACH (Mach's mit mir Gott)

OR

Based on the hymn tune by Johann Hermann Schein (1586-1630)

50 ELLACOMBE

OR

With majestic movement

Based on a melody from the Württemberg Gesangbuch (1784)

51 ELLERS

OR

Based on the hymn tune by Edward John Hopkins (1818-1901)

52 ES IST EIN' ROS' ENTSPRUNGEN

Based on a German carol

53 EVELYNS

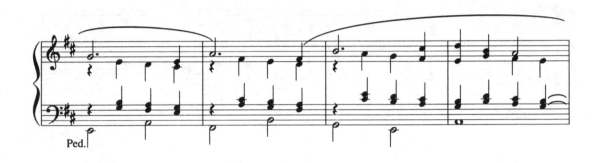

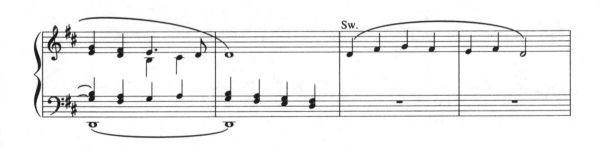

See over for another key

OR

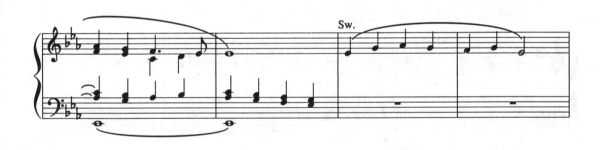

Based on the hymn tune by William Henry Monk (1823-1889)

54 EVENTIDE

Based on the hymn tune by William Henry Monk (1823-1889)

55 EWING

OR

Based on the hymn tune by Alexander Ewing (1830-1895)

56 FARLEY CASTLE

OR

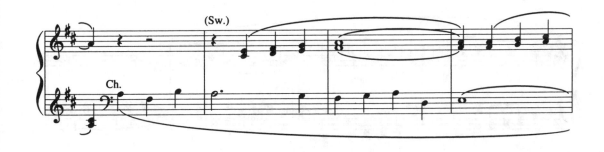

Based on the hymn tune by Henry Lawes (1596-1662)

57 FOREST GREEN

Based on a traditional English melody collected and arranged by Ralph Vaughan Williams (1872-1958)

58 FRANCONIA

Based on a melody from König's Harmonischer Lieder-Schatz (1738)
adapted by William Henry Havergal (1793-1870)

59 FULDA

94

OR

With vigour

f

rall.

Based on a melody from William Gardiner's Sacred Melodies (1815)

60 GERONTIUS

OR

Based on the hymn tune by John Bacchus Dykes (1823-1876)

61   GOD REST YOU MERRY

OR

Based on a traditional English carol

62 GONFALON ROYAL

Based on the hymn tune by Percy Buck (1871-1947)

63 GOPSAL

Based on the hymn tune by George Frideric Handel (1685-1759)

64 GREENSLEEVES

Based on a traditional English melody

65 GWALCHMAI

See over for another key

OR

Based on the hymn tune by Joseph David Jones (1827-1870)

66 HANOVER

Based on the hymn tune by William Croft (1678-1727)

67 HAREWOOD

OR

Based on the hymn tune by Samuel Sebastian Wesley (1810-1876)

68 HELMSLEY

With majestic movement

Based on a melody from John Wesley's Select Hymns (1765)

69 HEREFORD

See over for another key

Based on the hymn tune by Samuel Sebastian Wesley (1810-1876)

70 HERONGATE

See over for another key

OR

Based on a traditional English melody

71 HIGHWOOD

Based on the hymn tune by Richard Runciman Terry (1865-1938)

72 HOLLINGSIDE

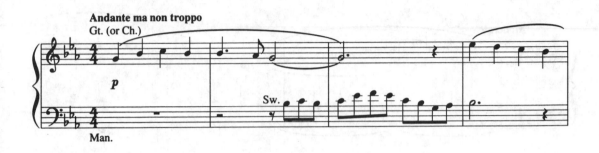

Based on the hymn tune by John Bacchus Dykes (1823-1876)

73 HORSLEY

See over for another key

OR

Based on the hymn tune by William Horsley (1774-1858)

74 HYFRYDOL

Based on the hymn tune by Rowland Huw Pritchard (1811-1887)

75 IRBY

OR

Based on the hymn tune by Henry John Gauntlett (1805-1876)

76 IRISH

OR

Based on a melody from A Collection of Hymns and Sacred Poems (1749)

77 KILMARNOCK

OR

Based on the hymn tune by Neil Dougall (1776-1862)

78 KING'S LYNN

With majestic movement

Based on a traditional English melody collected and arranged by Ralph Vaughan Williams (1872-1958)
© Copyright Oxford University Press (from the English Hymnal)

79 KINGSFOLD

Based on a traditional English melody collected and arranged by Ralph Vaughan Williams (1872-1958)

© Copyright Oxford University Press (from the English Hymnal)

125

80 LASST UNS ERFREUEN

OR

Con moto maestoso

Gt. *f*

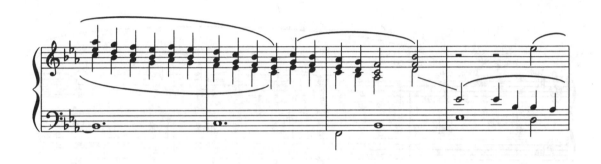

rall.

Based on a melody from the Geistliche Kirchengesäng (1623)

81 LAUDATE DOMINUM

Based on the hymn tune by Hubert Parry (1848-1918)

82 LAUDES DOMINI

See over for another key

OR

Based on the hymn tune by Joseph Barnby (1838-1896)

83 LAUS DEO (Redhead No. 46)

See over for another key

OR

Based on the hymn tune by Richard Redhead (1820-1901)

84 LEONI

See over for another key

133

OR

Based on a traditional Hebrew melody

85 LITTLE CORNARD

Based on the hymn tune by Martin Shaw (1875-1958)

© Copyright J. Curwen & Sons Ltd.

86 LLANFAIR

OR

Based on the hymn tune by Robert Williams (1781-1821)

87 LOBE DEN HERREN

OR

Based on a melody from Praxis Pietatis Melica (1668)

88 LOVE DIVINE

Based on the hymn tune by John Stainer (1840-1901)

89 LOVE UNKNOWN

See over for another key

OR

Andante con moto

Based on the hymn tune by John Ireland (1879-1962)

90 LUCKINGTON

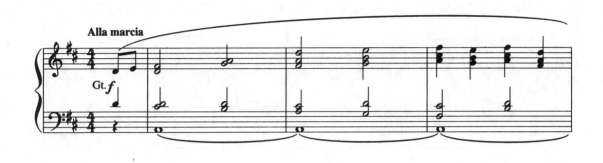

Based on the hymn tune by Basil Harwood (1859-1949)

Used by permission of the Executors of the late Dr Basil Harwood

91 LUX EOI

Based on the hymn tune by Arthur Sullivan (1842-1900)

92 MACCABAEUS

See over for another key

OR

Based on the hymn tune by George Frideric Handel (1685-1759)

93 MANNHEIM

See over for another key

OR

Based on the hymn tune by Friedrich Filitz (1804-1876)

94 MARCHING

Based on the hymn tune by Martin Shaw (1875-1958)

95 MARTYRDOM

Based on the hymn tune by Hugh Wilson (1766-1824)

96 MELCOMBE

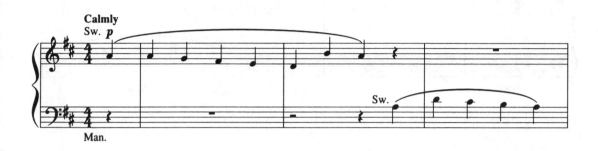

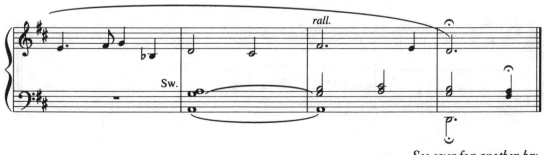

See over for another key

OR

Based on the hymn tune by Samuel Webbe (1740-1816)

97 MELITA

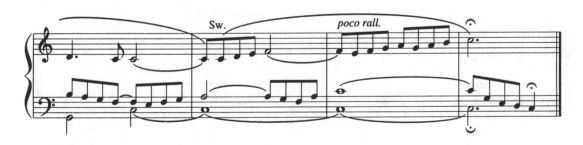

Based on the hymn tune by John Bacchus Dykes (1823-1876)

OR

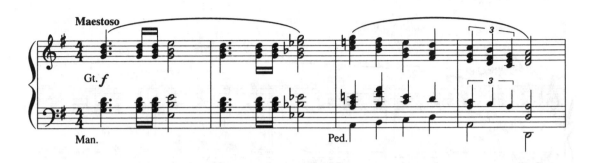

Based on the hymn tune by Felix Mendelssohn (1809-1847)

99 MERTON

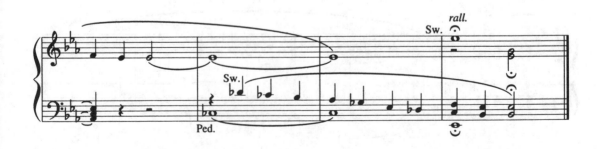

OR

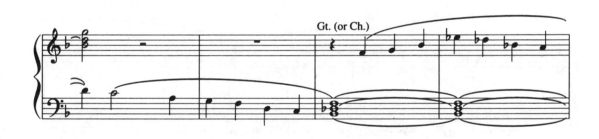

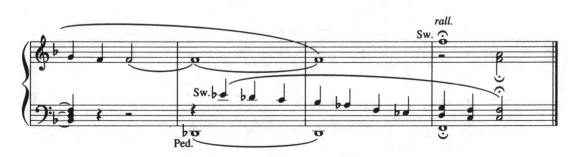

Based on the hymn tune by William Henry Monk (1823-1889)

100 MICHAEL

Based on the hymn tune by Herbert Howells (1892-1983)

101 MILES LANE

See over for another key

OR

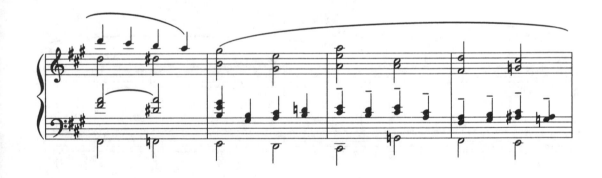

Based on the hymn tune by William Shrubsole (1760-1806)

102 MONKLAND

Based on the hymn tune by John Antes (1740-1811)

103 MONKS GATE

OR

Based on a traditional English melody collected and arranged by Ralph Vaughan Williams (1872-1958)

163

104 MORNING HYMN

Based on the hymn tune by François Barthélémon (1741-1808)

105 MORNING LIGHT

See over for another key

OR

Based on the hymn tune by George James Webb (1803-1887)

166

106 MOSCOW

Based on the hymn tune by Felice de Giardini (1716-1796)

107 MOUNT EPHRAIM

Based on the hymn tune by Benjamin Milgrove (1731-1810)

108 NARENZA

Based on a melody from Leisentritt's Catholicum Hymnologium Germanicum (1584)
adapted by William Henry Havergal (1793-1870)

109 NATIVITY

Based on the hymn tune by Henry Lahee (1826-1912)

110 NEANDER

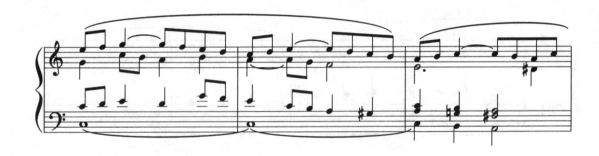

Based on the hymn tune by Joachim Neander (1650-1680)

111 NICAEA

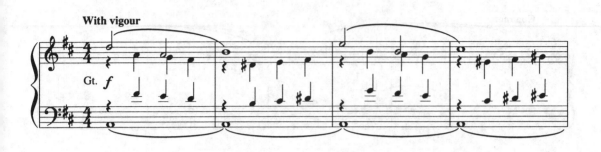

Based on the hymn tune by John Bacchus Dykes (1823-1876)

112 NOEL

Based on a traditional English melody adapted by Arthur Sullivan (1842-1900)

113 NOEL NOUVELET

OR

based on a traditional French melody

114 NUN DANKET

OR

Based on the hymn tune by Johann Crüger (1598-1662)

115 OBIIT

Based on the hymn tune by Walter Parratt (1841-1924)

116 OFFERTORIUM

Based on the hymn tune by Michael Haydn (1737-1806)

117 O FILII ET FILIAE

Based on a melody from Airs sur les hymnes sacrez (1683)

118 OLD HUNDREDTH

Based on a melody from the Genevan Psalter (1551)

119 OLD 104th

Based on the hymn tune by Thomas Ravenscroft (c.1590-1633)

120   OLD 120th

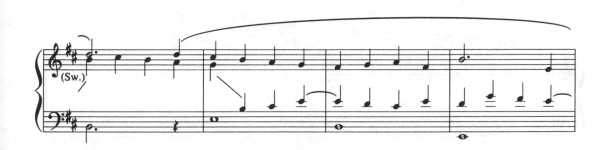

Based on a melody from Este's Psalter (1592)

121 ORIEL

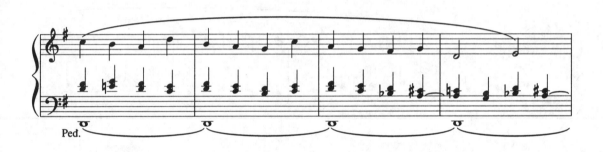

Based on the hymn tune by Caspar Ett (1788-1847)

122 PADERBORN

Based on a melody from the Paderborn Gesangbuch (1765)

123 PASSION CHORALE

Based on the hymn tune by Hans Leo Hassler (1564-1612)

124 PERSONENT HODIE

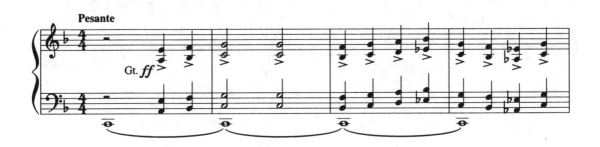

See over for another key

OR

Based on a melody from Piae Cantiones (1582)

125 PETRA

See over for another key

OR

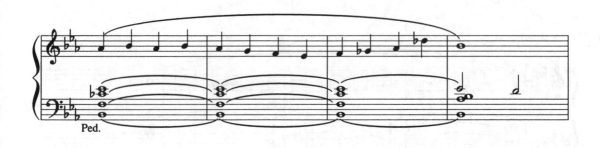

Based on the hymn tune by Richard Redhead (1820-1901)

126 PICARDY

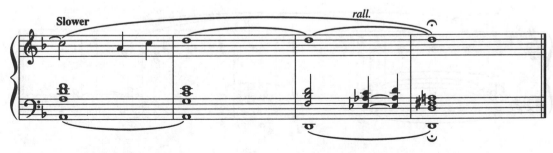

Based on a traditional French carol

127 PRAISE MY SOUL

Based on the hymn tune by John Goss (1800-1880)

128 PUER NOBIS NASCITUR

See over for another key

OR

Based on the hymn tune by Michael Praetorius (1571-1621)

129 QUAM DILECTA

Based on the hymn tune by Henry Lascelles Jenner (1820-1898)

130 QUEM PASTORES

Based on a traditional German melody (14th century)

131 RATISBON

Based on a melody from Johann Gottlob Werner's Choralbuch (1815)

132 RAVENSHAW

OR

Based on a medieval German melody adapted by William Henry Monk (1823-1889)

133 REGENT SQUARE

OR

Based on the hymn tune by Henry Smart (1813-1879)

134 REPTON

Based on the hymn tune by Hubert Parry (1848-1918)

135 REX GLORIAE

Maestoso con moto

See over for another key

203

Maestoso con moto

Based on the hymn tune by Henry Smart (1813-1879)

136 RHUDDLAN

Based on a melody from Edward Jones' Musical Relicks of Welsh Bards (1800)

OR

Based on the hymn tune by Thomas Haweis (1734-1820)

138 ROCKINGHAM

Based on a traditional English melody

139 ROYAL OAK

See over for another key

OR

Based on a traditional English melody

140 SAFFRON WALDEN

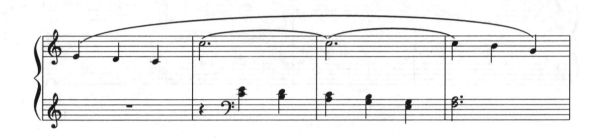

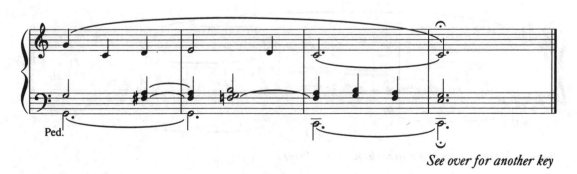

See over for another key

OR

Based on the hymn tune by Arthur Henry Brown (1830-1926)

141 ST ANNE

Based on a melody from A Supplement to the New Version (1708)
probably by William Croft (1678-1727)

142 ST BERNARD

Based on a melody from Tochter Sion (1741)

143 ST CLEMENT

See over for another key

OR

Based on the hymn tune by Clement Cotterill Scholefield (1839-1904)

144 ST COLUMBA

Based on a traditional Irish melody

145 ST DENIO

218

OR

Based on a Welsh melody from John Roberts' Caniadau y Cyssegre (1839)

146 ST EDMUND

Based on the hymn tune by Edward Gilding (d.1782)

147 ST FLAVIAN

Based on a melody from Ancient Hymn Melodies (1859)

148 ST FRANCIS XAVIER

OR

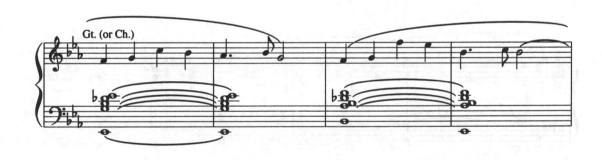

Based on the hymn tune by John Stainer (1840-1901)

149 ST FULBERT

OR

Based on the hymn tune by Henry John Gauntlett (1805-1876)

150 ST GEORGE'S WINDSOR

Based on the hymn tune by George Job Elvey (1816-1893)

151 ST HELEN

Based on the hymn tune by George Clement Martin (1844-1916)

152 ST JOHN DAMASCENE

Based on the hymn tune by Arthur Henry Brown (1830-1926)

153 ST MAGNUS

Based on the hymn tune by Jeremiah Clarke (c.1673-1707)

154 ST MATTHEW

Based on the hymn tune by William Croft (1678-1727)

155 ST PETER

See over for another key

Based on the hymn tune by Alexander Robert Reinagle (1799-1877)

156 ST STEPHEN

Based on the hymn tune by William Jones (1726-1800)

157 ST THEODULPH

OR

Based on the hymn tune by Melchior Teschner (1584-1635)

158 ST THOMAS

Based on the hymn tune by Samuel Webbe (1740-1816)

159 SALZBURG

Based on the hymn tune by Jacob Hintze (1622-1702)

160 SANDYS

OR

Based on a melody from William Sandys' Christmas Carols (1833)

161 SAVANNAH

Based on a melody from John Wesley's Foundery Collection (1742)

162 SHIPSTON

Based on a traditional English melody

163 SING HOSANNA

OR

With vigorous movement

Based on a traditional melody

164 SLANE

Based on a traditional Irish melody

165 SONG 1

Based on the hymn tune by Orlando Gibbons (1583-1625)

166 SONG 22

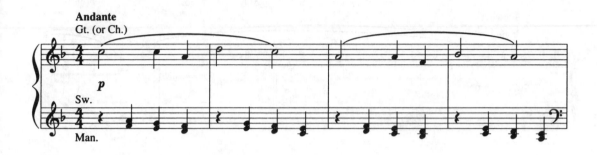

Based on the hymn tune by Orlando Gibbons (1583-1625)

167 SONG 34 (Angels' Song)

See over for another key

OR

Based on the hymn tune by Orlando Gibbons (1583-1625)

168 SOUTHWELL

Based on a melody from The Psalmes in English Metre (1579)
adapted by William Daman (1540-1591)

169 STILLE NACHT

Based on the hymn tune by Franz Grüber (1787-1863)

170 STOCKTON

Based on the hymn tune by Thomas Wright (1763-1829)

171 STRACATHRO

Based on the hymn tune by Charles Hutcheson (1792-1860)

172 STRENGTH AND STAY

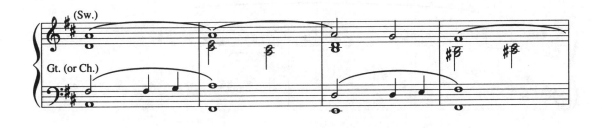

Based on the hymn tune by John Bacchus Dykes (1823-1876)

173 STUTTGART

OR

Based on the hymn tune by Christian Friedrich Witt (1660-1716)

174 SURREY

Based on the hymn tune by Henry Carey (c.1690-1743)

175 SUSSEX CAROL

Based on a traditional English melody

176 TALLIS'S CANON

Based on the hymn tune by Thomas Tallis (c.1505-1585)

177 TALLIS'S ORDINAL

Based on the hymn tune by Thomas Tallis (c.1505-1585)

178 THE FIRST NOWELL

Based on a traditional English carol

179 THIS JOYFUL EASTERTIDE

See over for another key

Based on a Dutch melody from David's Psalmen (1685)

180 THORNBURY

Based on the hymn tune by Basil Harwood (1859-1949)

Used by permission of the Executors of the late Dr Basil Harwood

181 TRURO

Based on a melody from Thomas Williams' Psalmodia Evangelica (1789)

264

182 UNIVERSITY

Based on the hymn tune by Charles Collignon (1725-1785)

183 UNIVERSITY COLLEGE

Based on the hymn tune by Henry John Gauntlett (1805-1876)

184 VENI EMMANUEL

Based on a melody from a French Missal adapted by Thomas Helmore (1811-1890)

185 VENI SANCTE SPIRITUS

Based on the hymn tune by Samuel Webbe (1740-1816)

186 VICTORY

*Based on a melody from Palestrina's Magnificat Tertii Toni (1591)
adapted by William Henry Monk (1823-1889)*

187 VULPIUS

Based on the hymn tune by Melchior Vulpius (c.1560-1615)

188 WAREHAM

See over for another key

271

OR

Based on the hymn tune by William Knapp (1698-1768)

189 WAS LEBET

See over for another key

Based on a melody from the Rheinhardt MS (1754)

190 WERE YOU THERE

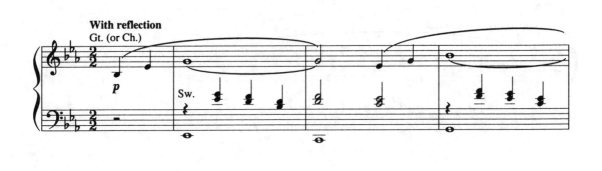

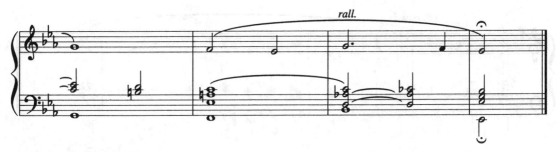

Based on an American folk melody

191 WESTMINSTER

Based on the hymn tune by James Turle (1802-1882)

192 WESTMINSTER ABBEY

See over for another key

OR

Based on the hymn tune by Henry Purcell (c.1659-1695)

193 WILTSHIRE

Based on the hymn tune by George Thomas Smart (1776-1867)

194 WINCHESTER NEW

Based on a melody from Musicalisches Hand-Buch (1690)

195 WINCHESTER OLD

Based on a melody from Thomas Este's Psalter (1592)

196 WIR PFLÜGEN

OR

Based on the hymn tune by Johann Abraham Peter Schulz (1747-1800)

197 WOLVERCOTE

Based on the hymn tune by William Ferguson (1874-1950)

198 WOODLANDS

Based on the hymn tune by Walter Greatorex (1877-1949)

© Copyright Oxford University Press

199 WÜRTTEMBERG

OR

Based on a melody from Hundert Arien (1694)

287

200 YORKSHIRE

Based on the hymn tune by John Wainwright (1723-1768)